Idiom
Stories

Compiled by Wu Min

CHINA INTERCONTINENTAL PRESS

图书在版编目（CIP）数据

中国成语故事：英文/伍民编；王国振，汉定，吴晓芳译．–北京：
五洲传播出版社，2011.1(2012.6重印)
（中国经典故事系列）
ISBN 978-7-5085-1773-5

Ⅰ.①中⋯ Ⅱ.①伍⋯ ②王⋯ ③汉⋯ ④吴⋯ Ⅲ.①汉语–
成语–故事–英文 Ⅳ.①H136.3

中国版本图书馆CIP数据核字(2012)第106464号

出　版　人：荆孝敏
编　　　者：伍　民
翻　　　译：王国振　汉　定　吴晓芳
责 任 编 辑：王　莉
设 计 指 导：缪　惟
设 计 制 作：吴俊宏
插　　　图：李思东

中国成语故事

出版发行：五洲传播出版社
社　　址：北京市海淀区莲花池东路北小马厂6号
邮政编码：100038
发行电话：010-82001477
制版单位：北京锦绣圣艺文化发展有限公司
印　　刷：北京圣彩虹制版印刷技术有限公司
开　　本：787x1092　1/32
印　　张：5.25
版　　次：2011年1月第1版　2012年6月第2次印刷
书　　号：ISBN 978-7-5085-1773-5
定　　价：53.00元

Preface

The term idiom refers to a set phrase formed through long-term usage. Chinese idioms have a fixed structure and parlance, with specific meaning. Most are composed of four characters, although some have three characters and a few consist of more than four. Some idioms are divided into two parts with a comma in the middle.

The Chinese idiomatic tradition boasts many rich contents, generally including its origin, literary quotation and historical fact. The splendid historical segments form the most vivid and interesting part of the idiom as a whole. Chinese idiom stories have inherited and passed on the abundant historic treasury of the Chinese nation that has been accumulated over several thousand years, mirroring the politics, military affairs, culture, folk customs, prevailing moral practices, ideals and interests of ancient China. Through these stories, people can gain an understanding of China s long history and achieve an insight into the profound historical origins of Chinese culture.

Compared with common Chinese words and expressions, the Chinese idioms, representing an important part of the Chinese language, feature salient strong points, i.e. they are concise, comprehensive, vivid and forceful, and have a precise structure. All languages have their own idioms. But the Chinese language boasts a larger numbers of idioms with a longer history, wider application, more outstanding status and more distinctive national culture. Even today, these idioms still play a significant role in the daily linguistic communication of the people. No matter whether Chinese or foreigner, anyone who intends to master the Chinese language and understand Chinese culture has to set store by the learning of Chinese idioms.

This book presents some 40 of the most common and enlightening idiom stories and offers them to the general reader with a combination of both fine illustrations and well laid-out texts, with a view to helping our friends from overseas cultivate their interest in learning about and understanding Chinese culture.

May this book be your good teacher and helpful friend in learning Chinese and practicing eloquence!

CONTENTS

Idiom Stories

The Eight Immortals Cross the Sea

Legend has it that the Eight Immortals came across the boundless East China Sea with its turbulent waves on the way to attend the Peach Party hosted by the Queen Mother of the West. However, they were glad at the chance to demonstrate their special skills.

Lu Dongbin said, "Since the East China Sea has immortal mountains and beautiful scenery, how about going there to take a look for ourselves? And it is forbidden to take a boat!"

All agreed with great pleasure and

prepared to cross the sea. Han Zhongli hurled his palm-leaf fan into the waters and lay on his back with the chest and abdomen exposed, floating forwards through the waves; He Xiangu cast a water lily into the sea, which at once emitted a powerful red glow, and she stood upon it to float across the waves; Tieguai Li threw his crutch into the sea and used it as a raft; Han Xiangzi cast out a decorated basket and piloted it as though it were a ship; and Lu Dongbin, Lan Caihe, Zhang Guolao and Cao Guojiu together threw their personal magic instruments into the sea which immediately turned into sampans. Thus all of them successfully crossed the stormy East China Sea. The idiom "The Eight Immortals Cross the Sea" originates from this legend.

The story comes from *Journey to the East*. It is used to symbolize the completion of a difficult task through one's own special method or skills.

拔苗助长

Help the Crops Grow by Pulling Them Upward

Help the Crops Grow by Pulling Them Upward

An ancient Chinese man called Mencius once told this story:

There was a farmer from the Song State growing a stretch of crops. He was convinced that his crops grew more slowly than those of his neighbors. He went to look at his field every day, wishing that his crops would grow faster.

Though many days passed, it seemed that the seedlings hadn't grown higher. He strode around the field impatiently and pondered, "I must get an idea to help them grow faster."

One day he finally came up with a solution. He started to pull the crops up. The peasant worked very hard the whole day and was physically exhausted but mentally happy. After coming back home, he gasped to his son, "I was totally tired today, but I didn't beat the air, and I helped the seedlings grow a little higher!"

His son was confused by his words and went to the field only to discover that all of his crops were dead.

The story is from *Mencius*. It indicates that handling affairs in spite of nature just makes a mess of things.

百发百中

A Hundred Shots, A Hundred Bull's-Eyes

A Hundred Shots, A Hundred Bull's-Eyes

In the Spring and Autumn Period (770 BC-476 BC) there was a famous archer in the Chu State called Yang Youji.

At one time, the Jin Ligong (Duke Li of Jin) made an attack on the Zheng State. Chu Gongwang (King Gong of the State Chu) dispatched troops to help the Zheng State and met the Jin army at Yanling. In the ensuing fight, a general of the Jin State called Wei Qi saw Chu Gongwang and shot an arrow at his eye. Chu Gongwang, who hated Wei Qi, gave two arrows to Yang Youji, saying, "Shoot Wei Qi to death to give me revenge over him." Without any word, Yang took the arrows and left. After a while, he came back with one arrow remaining and handed it back to Chu Gongwang. One arrow was all he had needed to kill Wei Ji.

At that time, another man named Pan Dang was also proficient in archery. He never missed the bull's eye in any competition. However, Yang Youji said to him, "This is not what it means to be a perfect marksman. The one who can shoot the leaf of willow at a distance of over one hundred paces—he can be regarded as a true marksman."

Pan Dang was not convinced. He selected three leaves on a willow and painted them with numbers so that Yang Youji could select his target. Yang Youji shot three consecutive arrows, hitting the three leaves in the prescribed order. Pan Dang was then sincerely convinced.

This story comes from *Strategies of the Warring States*. It is used to demonstrate perfect marksmanship. It also refers to great accuracy in predicting situations, thus succeeding in handling political or business affairs.

Seeing Is Believing

During the reign of Emperor Xuandi of
the Western Han Dynasty (206 BC-25 AD),
the Qiang people (one of the ethnic minorities
at that time) often appeared and disappeared
in the northwest border areas; they harassed
the local residents, attacked the towns and
slew the officials. Knowing this, the court
immediately held a meeting to discuss
countermeasures. All the ministers advocated
immediately sending troops to suppress the
Qiang people. However, when Emperor
Xuandi asked who could lead such an army,

nobody replied.

A 76-year-old general named Zhao Chongguo came forward and said that he would like to go to the northwest border areas to make reconnaisance. Emperor Xuandi was very pleased and said to him, "How many forces, weapons and provisions do you estimate you will need? Please tell me!"

Zhao Chongguo said, "It is hard to make a correct estimation and lodge specific requirements since I am not aware of the real situation. Seeing is believing. I would like to go there myself and have a look and find out the situation. Then I will inform Your Majesty."

Zhao Chongguo went to Jincheng County in northwest China to make a field survey and crossed the Yellow River to spy out the situation of the areas of the Qiang people. He also inquired of captives about the relations among the heads of the Qiang troops. Thus informed, he proposed the strategy of sending troops to the frontier to guard instead of making attack and suggested the policy of disconcerting the Qiang enemies by striving for harmony. Emperor Xuandi, however, listened to the opinions of other ministers and still stood for attack.

Zhao Chongguo disagreed and argued strongly on just grounds, listing the 12 advantages of his proposal and the 12 disadvantages of attack. After Zhao had presented communiques to the emperor many times and the emperor and ministers had discussed it repeatedly, the proportion of ministers in favor of Zhao Chongguo gradually increased to five tenths from three tenths and finally to eight tenths. Emperor Xuandi at last agreed to the proposal of Zhao Chongguo. As a result, the implementation of Zhao's proposal brought about a situation of peace and harmony between Han people and Qiang people, resulting in stabilized relations.

The idiom is from *Chronicles of the Han Dynasty: Biography of Zhao Chongguo*, meaning that it is better to see for oneself rather than to hear many times second-hand.

Spoil the
Half-finished Cloth

In the Eastern Han Dynasty (25-220), there was a man called Yue Yangzi in Henan Prefecture. Fortunately he had a kind wife whose name, unfortunately, remains unknown.

One day, Yue Yangzi picked up a piece of gold. Gladly, he rushed back home to show it to his wife. However, his wife said, "I hear that the one with ambition doesn't drink the water of Dao Spring (Robber Spring) because its name sounds disgusting and he would rather starve to death than eating food given by the people who disrespect him and wouldn't pick up the thing others lost because these would damage their morality." Yue Yangzi was very ashamed after hearing his wife's words and threw the piece of gold off into the fields and went to study in a far place.

One year later, Yue Yangzi came back home. His wife asked him the reason for his return. Yue said, "I was homesick and miss you very much, having been away for such a long time."

After hearing what Yue said, his wife took up a scissors and walked to the loom, saying, "To weave cloth, I first reel the silk thread off cocoons and then weave the cloth with one after another silk thread inch by inch. If I snip the clothes, all my previous efforts are wasted."

She continued, "Studying is also like this. You should acquire new knowledge every day, thus making your morality better and better. You come back leaving your studies unfinished, which is just the same as spoiling the half-finished cloth."

Yue Yangzi was deeply moved by his wife's words. Then, he went back to his studies and didn't return home for seven consecutive years.

This idiom comes from *Book of Rites: Doctrine of the Golden Mean*. It refers to giving up halfway.

不耻下问

Never Ashamed to Consult One's Inferiors

Never Ashamed to Consult One's Inferiors

During the Spring and Autumn Period (770 BC-476 BC) a senior official of the Wei State called Kong Yu was very modest but keen to learn.

After Kong Yu died, the King of the Wei State conferred the title "Wen (civilization)" upon him. Subsequently, people called him "Kong Wenzi" as a mark of respect.

Confucius (511 BC-479 BC) was a well-known philosopher, who had many students.

One student of his, called Zigong, was also a citizen of the Wei State. He thought that Kong Yu wasn't worthy of the high appraisement bestowed uopn him by the people.

One day, Zigong asked Confucius, "Why has the King of the Wei State conferred the title of Wen upon Kong Yu?"

Confucius answered, "Kong Yu was quick-minded and eager to learn and often consulted the people in a lower position and never felt ashamed to do so, so he was granted with this title."

After hearing that, Zigong was convinced and thought Kong Yu was worthy of the title.

This idiom is from *The Analects: Gongye Chang*, which states, "Quick-minded and eager to learn, he is never ashamed to consult his inferiors." It is often used to describe humility and a sense of curiousity.

How Can You Catch Tiger Cubs Without Entering the Tiger's Lair

A famous general called Ban Chao of the Eastern Han Dynasty (25-220) was sent to visit the Western Regions. He led 36 men to Shanshan State to express the desire of the Han Dynasty for establishing friendly relations with the State. The king of Shanshan was friendly to them in the beginning but suddenly, with no explanation, gave them the cold shoulder. As a matter of fact, messengers from the Huns had also come to the Shanshan State at that time and provoked animosity between the Han Dynasty and the Shanshan

State. The king of Shanshan began to hesitate.

Ban Chao, upon seeing this, called together his 36 men and said to them, "It is extremely dangerous for us now. The king of Shanshan has already acted coldly towards us. If the matter develops like this further, Shanshan might seize us and hand us over to the Huns. In that case, we won't be able to complete our mission and will die without a burial place!"

The 36 men asked, "So what should we do now? We all listen to you!"

Ban Chao said, "Just as you can't catch a tiger's cub unless you enter into its lair, it would be better to kill the Hun's messenger at night!"

At night, Ban Chao led the 36 heroes to the battalion of the Hunnish messengers, making a sudden attack on them. After a furious fight, Ban Chao and the 36 men killed over 100 Huns.

Ban Chao met with the King the next day and told him about the event. Realizing that they were extraordinarily brave, the King admired him and at the same time was afraid of them, signing the peace treaty with the Han Dynasty at once.

This story comes from *Later Chronicles of the Han Dynasty: Biography of Ban Chao*. The idiom indicates that one can not expect to achieve anything if one risks nothing and has no hard practice.

草木皆兵

Every Bush and Tree Look Like an Enemy

Every Bush and Tree Look Like an Enemy

In the Eastern Jin Dynasty (317-420), the king of Former Qin Fu Jian led an army to attack Jin State south of the Yangtze River. The Jin generals Xie Shi and Xie Xuan mustered 80,000 soldiers to counterattack. Fu Jian wanted to take the chance to defeat the Jin army rapidly, since it was much smaller in number.

In October of the same year, the Qin army occupied Shouyang Town and exploited the victory to besiege Xie Shi. Fu Jian led 8,000 hand-picked troops to Shouyang to spearhead the campaign. However, Xie Xuan took the opportunity to send General Liu Laozhi to assault Luojian with 5,000 troops, killing 10,000 Qin soldiers. The Qin army was badly beaten and its morale severely shaken; the soldiers were utterly demoralised. Fu Jian himself had not expected that the Jin army had such mighty battle effectiveness. He quickly climbed up the city wall of Shouyang to observe the Jin army, only to witness a formidable battle array aligned against him. And then, looking at the Bagongshan Mountain in the north, he mistook the grass and trees there for enemy soldiers, saying, "What a strong army! How can anyone say that it is lacking in numbers?" He began to regret having underestimated the enemy.

Subsequently, he established his troops on the northern bank of the Feishui River. At that time, Xie Xuan asked whether the Qin army could back off a little so as to allow the Jin army to cross the river and do battle. Fu Jian snickered that the Jin generals were ignorant of the basic principles of military tactics and intended to make a sudden attack on the Jin troops when they were busy crossing the river, and so he jumped at the offer made by the Jin army. However, immediately after the order of recession was issued, the Qin troops backed off like tidewater and were comprehensively routed because the troops behind were not aware of why they were backing off and assumed the forward troops had been defeated. The Qin troops were even trampled to death in the stampede. The Jin troops, meanwhile, took the opportunity to cross the river and persue the enemy, killing large numbers. Fu Jian was hit by an arrow but escaped to Luoyang. On the way, he shook with fear at the mere rustle of leaves in the wind. Soon, the former Qin Dynasty collapsed.

The story is from *History of the Jin Dynasty: Biography of Fu Jian*. It is used to describe the state of extreme nervousness or alarm in one's own group.

打草惊蛇

Beat the Grass and Startle the Snake

Beat the Grass
and Startle
the Snake

In the Tang Dynasty (618-907), a terribly greedy county magistrate named Wang Lu took many bribes and practiced graft. A large number of his subordinates also learned from him, arousing the discontent of the common people.

One day, someone sent him a petition accusing his secretary of practicing graft and taking bribes. The magistrate trembled when he read the petition, thinking, "Isn't it accusing me? Aren't the crimes those which I have committed? How do they know?"

Wang Lu was so frightened that he forgot his proper role in handling the case. Instead of issuing a judgment, he couldn't help writing these words concerning the petition: "By beating the grass, you have startled me, as I am like a snake under the grass!"

The idiom comes from *Despicable Things of the Southern Tang State*. Its original meaning is that punishment can serve as a warning to others or that the frustration of one person arouses another person's fear. But people now use the idiom to indicate that imprudent and imprecise actions startle the adversary.

Great Minds Mature Slowly

In the late Eastern Han Dynasty (25-220), a person called Cui Yan was keen on fencing and often practiced martial arts. He began to read books such as *The Analects* at the age of 23. However, due to his diligence, he became a person of great learning with outstanding martial arts skills.

Subsequently, he followed Cao Cao, a famous militarist in the Three Kingdoms Period (220-228), giving counsel to him and making great contributions to his learning.

One year, Cao Cao decided to designate his youngest son Cao Zhi as the crown prince. Cui Yan spoke to Cao Cao, saying, "It has been a custom of designating the eldest son as the crown prince since ancient times. How can you designate Cao Zhi?" Though Cao Zhi was the son-in-law of Cui Yan, Cui didn't give unprincipled protection to him. Hence, Cao Cao respected him more.

Cui Lin, the younger brother of Cui Yan, didn't gain any particular accomplishments or win any fine reputation when he was young, so many people thought that he wasn't promising and even his relatives and friends looked down on him. However, Cui Yan thought highly of him and said to others, "Great talents take time to mature. Give Cui Lin some time!"

Subsequently, Cui Lin was appointed a very important position by the emperor and subsequently acted as minister of public works under Emperor Wendi of the Wei State (220-265).

The story is from *Records of the Three Kingdoms*. The idiom refers to the fact that a great talent takes time to mature and others will finally recognize his or her talent.

Shake Up the Pillow and Have a Good Sleep

During the Warring States Period (475 BC-221 BC), a man from Qi State called Meng Changjun boasted 3,000 men in his home, classified into three grades. The men of the senior grade could have meat and enjoy the luxury of a carriage when going out; those of the medium grade could have meat but were not provided with a carriage; and those of the lower grade were given only vegetables.

One day, a man called Feng Xuan came to the home of Meng. But Meng didn't pay much attention to Feng, treating him as a lower guest. Feng was extremely unhappy and made complaints everyday. After hearing this, Meng upgraded Feng to the position of senior guest and sent his mother food and daily commodities. Then, Feng Xuan stopped grouching.

At one time, Meng Changjun sent Feng Xuan to a place called Xue to collect the rent. But Feng Xuan not only did not collect the rent; he also said to the local people, "Meng Changjun knows you have had a poor harvest this year and is afraid that you will face great difficulties as a result, so he exempts all the ground rents." And then he burned all of the contracts in front of the local people. The people of Xue were therefore very grateful to Meng and Feng provided him with the reputation of "loving the people". Subsequently, when Meng was dismissed from his post of prime minister and went back to Xue, the local people waited for him at the roadside and welcomed him back warmly.

Meng Changjun was deeply moved, and appreciated Feng Xuan very much.

Shortly afterwards, Feng Xuan said to Meng Changjun, "A rabbit should have three bolt holes in which to hide itself so that it won't be caught by the hunter. Now, the place of Xue is one of your 'caves', but it is not safe enough! You can't have a secure rest here. I would like to find another two 'caves' for you so that you have three safe places to hide!"

Then, Feng Xuan went to Liang State and told the King of Liang State what a talented and virtuous person Meng Changjun was. After hearing this, the King of Liang State sent people with 500 kg of gold and 100 carriages ask Meng Changjun to act as his prime minister.

The news spread to Qi State. The King of Qi State was in a pucker at once and invited Meng Changjun back to act as prime minster with grand formality. Meanwhile, Feng Xuan helped Meng Changjun build an ancestral temple in Xue to guarantee its security.

After the ancestral temple was completed, Feng Xuan said to Meng, "Now three caves have been made. From today, you can have a good rest without fear of any disturbances!"

This story is from *Strategies of the Warring States*. The idiom is used to indicate that everything has been thoroughly prepared and there is nothing to be worried about.

邯郸学步

Learn From Others at the Expense of One's Own Ability

Learn From Others at the Expense of One's Own Ability

Legend has it that in the Warring States Period (475 BC - 221 BC) a young man from the State of Yan in North China heard that in Handan, the capital of Zhao State, the people's walking posture was especially nice. He was in envy of them and wanted to learn their style of walking.

Then one day he made the long journey and traveled to Handan.

When he arrived in Handan, he stayed on the streets all day, watching how the Handan people walked. He looked at and pondered the characteristics of their walking. Then he started following the people who he thought walked particularly gracefully and imitated them. He mimicked the way they lifted their legs, how they placed their feet and swung their arms. He spent a long time doing this and made great efforts to imitate them correctly.

He learned to how to take several steps from a person today, and from another person tomorrow, but still did not walk like the Handan people. He always felt that his own walking posture was not as graceful as theirs.

He thought, "Maybe I am too used to walking in my own way and this makes it impossible to truly walk as the Handan people do."

Then he tried to forget his own way of walking and begin again from scratch.

Every step he took, he concentrated on how to raise his legs and swing his waist and arms. He wanted to blend the movements together in one fluent action.

When he walked, he forgot to ponder,

while when pondering, he forgot to walk. As a result, he lost his head only succeeded in walking like a puppet.

Several months passed. He not only failed to learn the Handan posture, but also forgot his original walking style. By this time, he had spent all the money he had brought. He was so hungry he could hardly stand, never mind learning to walk like other people.

So he had to return home. But he couldn't recall his original walking posture. In the end, the young man had no choice but to crawl on his hands and knees all the way back to Yan.

This story comes from *Chuang Tze: Autumn Water*. Later people used it to describe those who do not have their own personality and creativity, but only mechanically copy others. They not only fail to learn from others, but also forget their own knowledge.

Fear of Disturbance in the Rear

During the rule of Emperor Xiaowen of the Northern Wei Dynasty (386-534), Li Chong served as prime minister. He was loyal and devoted to the court and dealt with things carefully and properly. The Emperor trusted him very much and let him handle any business as he saw fit.

Later Li Chong passed away. Losing his right-hand man all of a sudden, Emperor Xiaowen, lonely and desolate, was very unhappy. He did not know who he could let handle the affairs of state.

One day, Emperor Xiaowen went out and passed by the tomb of Li Chong. Looking at this tomb, the Emperor was reminded of Li Chong's loyalty and thoroughness and could not help grieving all over again. He said emotionally, "Li Chong was loyal, reliable, and high-minded. He could handle any business that I enjoined him. Even if I led the army and went into battle, I had no fear that any disturbance would occur in the court as long as Li Chong administered the government affairs. Then I had no worries of disturbance in the rear. Now he has passed away, and who can I depend on?"

This idiom comes from *Chronicles of the Northern Wei Dynasty: Biography of Li Chong*. It is used to describe a person who does not feel anxious about things at home or anticipate a disturbance in the rear.

后生可畏

A Youth to be Regarded With Respect

A Youth to be Regarded With Respect

The ancient Chinese philosopher and educator Confucius often traveled through all the states in order to give publicity to his theories.

One day, he took his carriage and went out on one of these journeys. Seeing a child in the middle of the road all of a sudden, he immediately asked the driver to halt. Confucius said to the child, "Can you please give way to my carriage?" The child pointed to the road, saying, "Can't you see that there is a castle here?"

Confucius looked where the child pointed and saw a small castle made of mud. The child continued, "I only heard that marriages move around a castle. I've never heard that a castle should give way to traffic." Confucius was much surprised and said admiringly, "At such a young age, you seem to know quite a lot."

The kid raised his head and looked directly at Confucius. He said, "I heard fish can swim as soon as they are born. Rabbits can run on the third day after birth. All these are natural phenomena. Age doesn't make a difference." Hearing this, Confucius felt the child's words were reasonable and said emotionally, "Oh, youngsters today are really remarkable."

Confucius asked the carriage driver to bypass the child's castle.

This Chinese idiom is excerpted from *The Analects*. It means that even a child is to be regarded with respect. The younger generation, full of youthful spirit, will often surpass their elders.

Swallow a Date
Whole

Once upon a time, a young person was walking along a road while eating a pear. Then an old doctor approached from the opposite direction.

The old doctor said to the young person, "Though tasty, the pear should not be eaten too much. It is good for the teeth, but too many will be bad for the spleen." Hearing the old man's words, the youngster put the pear away and took several dates from his pocket, saying, "So, I can eat dates but not pears, in order to protect my spleen. How about eating dates."

The old doctor replied, "The date has the function of nourishing the spleen, but eating dates too much will be bad for the teeth, so they should not be eaten in quantity."

After hearing what the old man said, the young man looked at the dates in his hand, hesitated, and did not know how to proceed.

After thinking for a while, he said, "What do you think of this way? When eating pears, we only chew them with our teeth, and spit them out instead of swallowing them. And when eating dates, we swallow them whole instead of chewing them. By doing this, both my teeth and my spleen will be unhurt." His words made the old doctor at a loss whether to laugh or cry. He did not know how to respond.

This story is excerpted from *Zhanyuan Jingyu*. It is used to describe those who mechanically take in what they study without understanding and analyzing what they are being taught.

Last Touch Added to a Drawing

During the Northern and Southern Dynasties (386-589) there was a famous painter named Zhang Sengyao. He was very good at painting. His paintings were vivid and true to life.

One year, Zhang painted four dragons on the wall in the Le'an Temple in Jinling (present-day Nanjing City). All of them were absolutely lifelike, attracting many sightseers.

All of a sudden, someone noticed a defect in them, saying, "Look, these dragons have no eyes."

The other people now looked at them more carefully and indeed saw that eyes had not been painted on them.

Then they found Zhang Sengyao and said, "You have not finished your paintings and why do the dragons have no eyes?"

"I cannot do that. If I draw the eyes, the dragons will fly off the wall," Zhang replied.

They laughed and felt that he talked nonsense. Some one said, "You are just talking big. How can painted dragons fly away? Draw eyes on them and let us see whether they can fly away."

The onlookers insisted that he add eyes to the dragons. Urged on by the crowd, Zhang added eyes to two of the dragons.

As soon as he finished, the sky became overcast and there was thunder and lightning. Accompanied by the thunder and lightning, the two dragons started to move and soon flew up into the sky. The people were too scared to ask him to add eyes to the remaining two dragons. Therefore, only two dragons are still to be seen on the wall of the Le'an Temple.

This story is excerpted from *Famous Painting in the Past Dynasties*. Now it means that when people make a speech or write an essay, adding several words or characters in the key part will enhance the whole.

Adding Feet to a Drawing of a Snake

During the Warring States Period (475 BC-221 BC), Zhao Yang, a general of the Chu State, made a clean sweep in attacking the Wei State. He then intended to fall upon the Qi State. Upon hearing this, the King of the Qi was so concerned that he sent Chen Zhen as a diplomatic envoy to advise Zhao Yang not to attack his state.

Chen Zhen met with Zhao Yang and said, "What reward will you get in accordance with your state rules for achieving such a great military victory?"

Zhao Yang complacently replied, "I will get a new promotion and be put in charge of military affairs, a position only below that of the monarch or a marquis." Chen Zhen asked, "Will you also be promoted to a more senior official position?"

"Yes, it will be Lingyin or the Prime Minister," said Zhao Yang.

Chen Zhen said, "In my opinion, the King of the Chu will not confer two Lingyin upon you. Let me tell you a story.

"A nobleman in the Chu State, after making offerings to his ancestors, took a bowl of wine that was left over from the offerings and gave it to his servants. They looked at the wine and thought if we all drink from this bowl of wine, each of us will just barely get a taste of it. It would be much better if all the wine went to one person. Of course, everyone wanted the wine for himself and they inevitably quarreled. Finally, they had a good idea: they would have a competition to draw a snake on the ground. The one who finishes drawing first will win the bowl of wine.

"Everyone squatted down on the ground and began to draw a snake. One of them finished his drawing quickly, took the pot of wine and was about to drink. He looked at the others, who were still not finished yet. Some were drawing the head and some the tail. He said contemptuously, 'How stupid you all are! I still have enough time to add feet to my snake.' Then he held the bowl in his left hand and drew feet for the snake with his right. But before he finished the feet, another man completed his own snake and grabbed the bowl from him, saying, 'Whoever has seen a snake with feet? Yours is not a snake. So the wine should be mine!' He drank the wine. The man who had added feet to the snake had to concede defeat and could only regret his foolishness.

"You have rendered meritorious service for the Chu State. But you do not want to stop while you are ahead and now want to assault the Qi State. In case of a mishap, don't you fear a calamity would happen to you? Isn't what you plan to do the same as adding feet to a drawing of a snake?"

Hearing Chen Zhen's words, Zhao Yang changed his mind.

This story comes from *Strategy II of the Qi State* in *Strategies of the Warring States*. Now people use this idiom to illustrate the truth that going too far is as bad as not going far enough.

Flashy But Without Substance

During the Spring and Autumn Period (770 BC-476 BC), Yang Chuwen, a senior official of the Jin State, had gone to Wei State on a mission of friendly inquiries, and on his return passed by Ning City of the Lu State. A person named Ning Ying in the Ning City took the chance to throw himself into his path, in the hope that he could serve as an official in the Jin State with Yang Chuwen's patronage.

They walked for several days, but when they reached the Wen area Ning Ying suddenly disappeared. Yang Chuwen had no idea where Ning Ying had gone.

The explanation was that Ning Ying felt that Yang Chuwen had behaved badly and so returned home.

His wife did not know why and asked him, "Didn't you want to follow Yang Chuwen to the Jin State and why did you return after only going half way?"

He replied, "Yang Chuwen is self-opinionated and extreme. Moreover, he likes talking big, painting the devil blacker than he is, and does not do real things. The person of this kind has all his goods in the window, and talks cleverly but is not prudent. He makes it very easy to contract enmity with others. He will probably not die a natural death because of these shortcomings. I was afraid I would not share in any advantages he might secure, but would most definitely be caught up in his difficulties, and so I left him."

A year later, Yang Chuwen was killed.

This story comes from *Fifth Year of the Reign of Emperor Wengong* in *Zuozhuan*

(*Master Zuo's Spring and Autumn Annals*). The Chinese character "华" (magnificent), is the same as "花" (flower). The idiom originally meant a flower without bearing fruit. Later it was used to describe a person or thing that is good in appearance, but worthless inside.

A Treasure Worth Several Cities

During the Warring States period (475 BC-221 BC) in ancient China, a peasant in the Wei State by accidentally came across a piece of unusual stone in the field he was farming. Though grotesque in shape, the stone was sparkling and crystal-clear and seemed to him very beautiful. He brought it home.

He went to his neighbor who was a jade artisan and asked him what kind of stone it was. His neighbor saw immediately that it was a piece of rare and precious jade, and wanted to keep it for himself. He then lied to the peasant, "This stone is very strange. Anyone who keeps it will have terrible things happen to him. You'd better put it back where you found it." The peasant didn't quite believe what his neighbor had told him. He did not throw it away immediately and took the stone home.

That night, after the lamp was put out, the stone emitted a bright beam of light all of a sudden, which scared the whole family. The peasant went to his neighbor and told him about it. His neighbor lied to him again, "This is a very bad sign. To avoid tragedy in your family, you must put it back where you found it." This time the peasant believed his neighbor completely and threw the stone away. The neighbor was very happy that the peasant had done as he said, and later snuck out to the field and picked up the jade, after which he went to the palace and presented it to the King.

At first, the King felt it did not amount to much. However, the jade artisan insisted that it was a piece of very precious jade. The King told an experienced jade carver to give his opinion. The old jade carver examined it and said to the King, "Congratulations, Your Majesty, this is a rare treasure indeed. I've never before seen jade as valuable." The king was very pleased to hear this. He asked the jade carver just how much the jade was worth. The jade carver answered, "It is a priceless treasure. Merely taking a look at it should cost the price of five cities." The king was very happy, and gave the peasant's neighbor a huge reward.

This Chinese idiom is from Yin Wenzi : Da Dao Shang. It is used to describe something very precious.

Official Jiang Uses Up His Literary Talent

There once lived a brilliant writer named Jiang Yan in the Liang State of the Northern and Southern Dynasties (386-589) Period. Because his family was very poor, he studied extremely hard when he was a child. Both his poems and his essays were outstanding, so he was thought very highly of by the Emperor and who then made him as a senior official.

As Jiang Yan grew older, the poems and essays that he wrote were not as good as those he had written when he was younger. People did not know the reason. However, there were two stories going around that tried to account for it.

Jiang Yan once passed by the Chanling Temple. He spent the night there and had a dream. In this dream, a man said to him, "Once upon a time, I left a piece of brocade to you and allowed you to use it for a certain number of years. Today you should give it back to me." Hearing his words, Jiang Yan drew out the brocade from his bosom and returned it to the man. From then on, the essays that he wrote became worse and worse.

Another time, Jiang Yan lived in the Yeting and dreamed of a person who said he was named Guo Pu. He said to Jiang Yan, "One of my pens has been here with you for several years. You have used it to write many good poems. And now you should give it back to me." Jiang Yan found a multi-colored pen in the folds of his cloak, which he returned to Guo Pu. From then on, the poems that Jiang Yan wrote were not as good as those he had written before.

Everyone said that he had used up the last of his talent.

This story is excerpted from *Biography of Jiang Yan* in *History of the Southern Dynasty*. The idiom originally meant that Jiang Yan had used up his literary talent. Later people expanded it to describe the going down of any person's creativity.

九牛一毛

A Hair on Nine Bulls

A Hair on Nine Bulls

Li Ling, a famous general during the rein of Emperor Wu of Han Dynasty (206 BC-220 AD), led his troop to attack the Huns. The general won a lot of battles after penetrating the territory of the Huns, but later failed and surrendered after his troop was severely beset by the Hun troop. Hearing the news, Emperor Wu was irritated, and the ministers also condemned Li Ling was incapable and disloyal.

Sima Qian, a renowned historian in the Chinese history, was wordless while others violently blamed Li Ling. Emperor Wu asked how he looked at Li Ling's surrender. Sima Qian told the truth: Li Ling only had 5,000 infantries, but was besieged by 80,000 cavalrymen; even in face of such an adversity, General Li still fought against the Huns for more than ten days, and killed over 10,000 enemy soldiers; so he was really an outstanding general; at last, General Li had to stop fighting when he used up his supply and got blocked from withdrawal; Li Ling might pretend to surrender so as to wait for an opportunity to be loyalty to the nation.

Hearing the historian official defend the failing general, Emperor was so angry to put him to prison. To flatter the emperor, Du Zhou, the supreme judicial official, said Sima Qian was guilty of framing the emperor, and imposed the cruelest and most insulting penalty—Fuxing (castration) on Sima Qian. After suffering such an insulting penalty, Sima Qian was so painful that he wanted to kill himself. However, he finally gave up the thought, considering his death was just like "a hair shed from nine bulls" in the eyes of many people, and nobody would care, so he would be mocked rather than having their sympathy. Therefore, he made up his mind to bear the insult and leave his life to complete *Shi Ji* (*Historical Records*), the lifelong wish of both his father and himself. In the end, he completed the greatest historical masterpiece —*Shi Ji*— in China with his disabled body.

This story is extracted from *A Letter to Answer Shaoqing Ren* (Shaoqing refers to a senior position), and this proverb is used to describe something that is a tiny part of many things, just like a hair on nine bulls.

A Dagger Heart Behind a Honey Mouth

Li Linfu, a prime minister during the Rein of Emperor Xuan in the Tang Dynasty (618-907), was kind to others in public, but always framed others in private.

He always tried to associate with those in power, but strived to get rid of those who were witted or stronger than him, or dispatch them to remote places.

He also gave glove money to people close to the emperor so that they would tell him what the emperor said. In this way, he could know who the emperor favored, and he would make a false charge against the person.

He once heard that the emperor thought highly of Lu Xuan, the assistant minister of war, so he assigned Lu Xuan to be the magistrate of Huazhou. However, he later said Lu Xuan was in poor health and unable to administer the government affairs and therefore demoted Lu. Another time, when the emperor wanted to appoint Yan Tingzhi to a higher position, he said to the emperor, "This person, old and weak, is now curing his disease. Though he is very capable, I'm afraid he can't live up to the position." Though the emperor felt very regretful, Li Linfu successfully realized his trick. The emperor had no idea at all his prime minister played tricks.

Despite his ill intention, Li Linfu was very kind to others in face, and always spoke with a honeyed mouth so that others would feel he was a good person. However, his heart was vicious as a dagger that could kill others. Therefore, people knowing him well said, "Li

Linfu has honey in the mouth but a dagger in the heart." Everybody hated him very much.

This story comes from *Zizhi Tongjian* (*History as a Mirror*), and the proverb is now used to describe those who are cunning with a honeyed mouth but an atrocious heart.

Make Up the Number

King Xuan, the king of the State Qi in the Warring States (475 BC-221 BC), enjoyed listening to the musical performance. Besides, he loved the symphony very much, so he built a band composed of up to 300 people. The band specially performed the music for the king.

A person, name Mr. Nanguo, was unable to play the musical instrument. Now that King Xuan liked the symphony, he mixed himself in the band to make a living. During each performance, he also pretended to be playing the musical instrument, and shook his head with the musical rhythm, as if he was playing the music. Thus, he passed off in the band for many years, but surprisingly, King Xuan didn't find this at all! After the death of King Xuan, his son became the king, and also liked listening to the musical performance. However, different from King Xuan, he didn't like the symphony but solo. So he ordered every member of the band to perform the music for him.

This time, Mr. Nanguo was very afraid that he would be revealed — after all, cheating the king would be a crime to be punished with the general penalty. Then, he escaped in private one night.

This story comes from *Han Feizi: A Collection of Historic Stories (Volume One)*. Now, people use this proverb to compare those who have no knowledge or are insiders but mix themselves among knowledgeable people or insiders. This proverb is also used to use describe the situation that the shoddy replace the quality, and also, some people use this proverb to express their modesty.

老马识途

An Old Horse Knows the Way

An Old Horse
Knows the Way

The State Yan in the Spring and Autumn Period (770 BC-476 BC), bordered Shan Rong, a horde sovereignty in the north.

One year, Shan Rong declared a war against the State Yan, which asked for help from the State Qi, a then power nation. King Huan of Qi and Guan Zhong, a famous reformer and militarist in the Spring and Autumn Period, led the army to rescue the State Yan.

The war started in spring, and lasted almost one year. Finally, they defeated Shan

Rong, and ran after into the State Guzhu. At that time, it was already winter. The Qi army were not familiar with the terrain in the State Guzhu. One day, the army entered into a valley surrounded by stiff mountains, and lost the way before they realized it.

King Huan of Qi was very anxious, and sent a few squads to look for the way out. However, how could they find the way out in face of the high mountains? The Qi army wandered in the valley once and again, but couldn't find the way out. If they couldn't go out, the confidence of the soldiers would be shaken, and even worse, and the army was likely to be raided by the enemy. King Huan of Qi was as anxious as a cat on hot bricks, but couldn't work out an idea.

Suddenly, Guan Zhong said to King Huan of Qi, "An old horse may know the way. We can select a few old horses, and let them walk ahead. Let's try whether we can get out of here."

King Huan of Qi was very glad, "A great

idea! Just do it!"

Guan Zhong chose a couple of old horses, unleashed them and made them walk ahead. The old horses looked around, and then walked along the hillside after they were free. The army followed the old horses, and finally walked out of the valley!

This story comes from *Han Feizi: A Collection of Stories (Volume One),* and now, this proverb is often used to compare those people who are familiar with the things and may act as the guide in work.

Extreme Joy Begets Sorrow

In the Warring States Period (475 BC-221 BC), King Wei of the State Qi often drank a lot and indulged himself throughout the night, which resulted into a crisis.

The State Chu used the opportunity to attack the State Qi. Fortunately, Chunyu Kun asked the State Zhao to rescue the State Qi, and avoided the disaster of the ruin. Therefore, King Wei of Qi prepared a feast to appreciate him.

At the feast, King Wei of Qi asked Chunyu Kun, "How much do you drink before you are drunk?"

Chunyu Kun answered, "I may get drunk after drinking a dou (an ancient Chinese measuring unit) of wine or a dan (also an ancient Chinese measuring unit, equal to ten dou) of wine."

King Wei of Qi felt very strange, "How come? Now that you are drunk after you drink a dou of wine, how can you drink a dan of wine?"

Chunyu Kun explained, "If you invite me to a drink, I will get drunk only after a dou of wine, because there are the law enforcement official near me and royal etiquette official behind, because I am nervous. However, if I drink together with good friends I haven't seen for a long time, I may drink five or six dou, because I am happy. If drinking at a private party where all the people sit together regardless of men or women, and entertain ourselves, I can drink even eight dou before I am drunk. And if the host retains me, I will feel very free, I like this moment the best, and so I can drink a dan of wine."

Then, he stopped, looked into the eyes of King Wei, and continued, "So, the ancient people say that if a person drinks too much, he will forget the etiquette; and if a person is joyful to the extreme, sorrow will follow."

Then King Wei realized Chunyu Kun was ridiculing him! He sighed, "You are right, sir!"

From then on, King Wei no longer drank or indulged himself throughout the night.

This proverb, which comes from *Historical Records: The Jesters*, means the extreme joy will beget sorrow. Sometimes, this proverb is also used to describe the truth that the time of extreme joy tends to be accompanied by sad things.

Green Willows and Red Flowers

Lu You, a patriotic poet in the Southern Song Dynasty (1127-1279), strongly claimed to resist the Jin Dynasty (265-420) and objected to compromise. However, the ministers who wanted to surrender strived to push him aside, and kept telling the emperor that Lu You only enjoyed flowers and wrote poems all day long, and loafed about every day. As a result, Lu You was dismissed to return home.

Full of irritation, Lu You returned to his hometown, and often enjoyed himself in the nature to release his sorrow.

One day, the wind was mild, the sun was shining and the temperature was pleasant, so Lu You wanted to relax himself on such a good day. After walking for more than two hours, he climbed a slope to see the mountain and waters ahead, forming magnificent views. However, there was no way leading to his destination. Invited by the views, Lu You didn't want to go back, so he continued making his way in the forest. After walking around the foot of the hill, he suddenly found a vast farmland ahead, and a small village with tens of households concealed in green willows and red flowers, just like the worry-free world in the fairy tale. Lu You was very glad, and entered the village to visit the villagers. The villagers also warmly entertained this guest from outside the hill, and the neighbors also entertained Lu You warmly, and prepared banquets to receive him. The simple folk customs moved Lu You very much. He was inspired to write a poem named *A Visit to a Village to the West of the Hill*.

The poem contains the following two lines: "Where hills bend, streams wind and the pathway seems to end past dark willows and flowers in bloom lies another village."

This proverb, which comes from *A Visit to a Village to the West of the Hill*, and originally means green willows that form shades and flowers blossom. Later, people often use this proverb to describe the situation that an opportunity occurs during a crisis.

Wind and Rain
Throughout the Town

There was a very talented poet, named
Pan Dalin, in the Song Dynasty (960-1279).
Talented as he was, he lived a very poor life.

Just like other poets who loved writing
poems to describe views, Pan also enjoyed
writing poems about views, the views in
autumn in particular.

One year, one of his friends wrote him
a letter, asking whether he had created some
good poems. He replied, "The views in
autumn are very special. Many poets have
written good poems about autumn, indicating

autumn is the season that gives birth to good works. However, our social style is not very good, and my interest in writing poems is often ruined."

"Take yesterday for example. I lay on the bed, looking at the continuous autumn rain and hearing the autumn wind, and thought it was very poetic. Then, I hurried to rise from the bed, and started to write a poem on the wall. However, just after my first sentence— The Double Ninth Festival is approaching amid the wind and rain across the town, I heard a loud knock at my door, and then a person broke in, and told me rudely, 'Pay your rent now!' My interest in writing the poem was completely ruined, so I will have to post this sentence to you."

This story comes from *A Night Talk at a Cold House*. The proverb originally describes the view of an autumn rain, and now is often used to render the fact that people will start discussing the news after it flies apace.

Falling After Sun Shan

There was a person called Sun Shan in the Song Dynasty (960-1279). One year, he sat the imperial examination, and a countryman asked his son to go with Sun Shan. Eventually, Sun Shan really succeeded, but his name ranked at the bottom on the list. The son of his countryman failed, became very depressed and asked Sun Shan to return first.

After returning home, his neighbors all came to see him, and congratulate his success.

The countryman didn't see the son had

Idiom Stories

come back, and asked Sun Shan about his son's examination.

The countryman said, "Congratulations! My son hasn't come back until now. How about his examination?" Sun Shan, a very humorous person, didn't give a direct answer, but replied humorously, "At the end of the ranking is Sun Shan, and your son even falls behind Sun Shan."

That is to say, Sun Shan ranked last on the list for admission, while the countryman's son even fell behind Sun Shan, meaning the son had failed.

This story comes from *A Record of Guoting*. Now, people use this proverb to compare the failure in an examination or election.

呕心沥血
Vomit Heart, Shed Blood

Vomit Heart,
Shed Blood

Li He, a very famous poet in the Tang
Dynasty (618-907), was very gifted, and
started writing articles at the age of seven.
After he grew up, he hoped with the whole
heart that the emperor would put him into an
important position. However, he had never
been successful in the political career. Feeling
very depressed, he bent himself on creating
poems to relieve the sorrow.

Every time he went out, he would ask
his servant to carry a bag. As long as he had
an inspiration and thought of a good poem, he
would immediately write it down and put it in

the bag. After returning home, he would sort up and refine his drafts. When his mother saw he had written so many poems, she would feel very distressed, "My son has spent all of his energies and emotions on writing poems. He won't give up until he vomits his heart."

Li He died at a young age of only twenty-six. During his life of twenty-six years, he had left more than two hundred and forty poems, all of which were created with his lifelong energies. Han Yu, a litterateur in the Tang Dynasty, had two sentences of the poem *A Return to Pengcheng* — Scoop the liver as paper, Shed blood as ink — which means removing the liver as paper, and shed blood to write articles.

This story comes from *Biography of Li He*. The proverb originally meant excess energies on writing articles, and later is used to describe sparing no efforts.

Cast a Brick to Invite a Jade

Zhao Gu was a poet in the Tang Dynasty (618-907). He was very gifted in writing poems, and hailed by Du Mu, a renowned poet in the Tang Dynasty.

At that time, there was another poet called Chang Jian, who also wrote good poems, but admired the works of Zhao Gu very much. One day, Zhao Gu traveled to Suzhou, and Chang Jian chanced to stay in Suzhou as well. Hearing the news, Chang Jian was overjoyed, and told himself, "This is a good opportunity I should not miss. I must have Zhao Gu leave some good poems."

However, he didn't know how to let Zhao Gu write poems he needed. Suddenly, he thought of Lingyan Temple, a place of wonder in Suzhou. Now that Zhao Gu arrived in Suzhou, he would definitely visit Lingyan Temple. If I write half a poem in the Temple, it may arouse the interest of Zhao Gu in finishing the poem. Then, Chang Jian wrote two lines on a wall of Lingyan Temple in private.

As expected by Chang Jian, Zhao Gu really paid a visit to Lingyan Temple the following day. Seeing there were only two lines of a poem on the wall, he thought it was very unnatural, and added another two lines to form a complete poem. Chang Jian used his two not-very-good lines to invite a wonderful poem consummated by Zhao Gu. Somebody said the method of Chang Jian was just like casting a brick to invite a jade.

This story comes from *Poetry of Past Generations*. Later, people use this proverb to describe the shallow and shoddy article that invites the perfect articles of others, mainly the opinions on poems and articles. This proverb is also often used to express modesty.

Breaking the Pot, Sinking the Boat

Hu Hai was the second emperor of Qin Dynasty (221 BC-206 BC). He dispatched Senior General Zhang Han to defeat the rebel army led by Chen Sheng and Wu Guang, and then attack the State Zhao after crossing the Yellow River.

The king of the State Zhao couldn't resist the Qin army, and asked the State Chu for support. The king of the State Chu agreed, and appointed Song Yi as the general and Xiang Yu as the assistant to rescue the State Zhao. When the Chu army arrived in Anyang,

Song Yi ordered to put up the tents, and refused to march ahead any more.

Afraid to have a decisive battle against the Qin army, Song Yi held troops for 46 days in succession. It was then a severe winter with cold wind and heavy snow. The soldiers were both cold and hungry, but Song Yi just enjoyed himself, regardless of the hardship of his soldiers.

Xiang Yu, an impatient person, didn't like Song Yi, and then killed him. After taking control of the army, he immediately sent 20,000 soldiers to cross the Zhanghe River to save the State Zhao. However, the army didn't win a great victory, so Xiang Yu led the army to cross the Zhanghe River in person.

Just coming ashore, Xiang Yu ordered the soldiers to sink all the boats, break all the pots and burn the camps, and carry the dry provision for three days only, telling soldiers they would no way to retreat, unless they won the victory.

Xiang Yu told his soldiers, "We will

launch a decisive battle against the enemy. Either your enemy die or you die. No victory, no return!"

Seeing the boats had been sunken, the pots had been broken and no leeway had been left, all the soldiers were prepared to fight regardless of their lives.

When meeting the Qin army, the Chu army immediately came at the Qin army and shouted aloud with great courage. Though the Qin army had won many battles, they had never seen such a fearless army, and got so frightened to turn around and run away. The Chu army fought very bravely, and defeated the Qin army completely.

This story, which comes from *Historical Records: Biography of Xiang Yu,* is later used to cut off the way of retreat, forcing oneself to march ahead without withdrawal.

The Guizhou Donkey Exhausts Its Tricks

Liu Zongyuan, a great litterateur in the Tang Dynasty (618-907), wrote a story below:

It was said that there were no donkeys in Guizhou, and a person shipped a donkey from other place to the foot of a Guizhou mountain.

A tiger in the mountain saw the donkey in a distance and wanted to eat the donkey.

However, the tiger had never seen such an animal before. Seeing the donkey was tall and large, the tiger didn't know the power of the donkey, and thus was a little afraid. The tiger was afraid to be too close to the donkey, but hid in the forest in private, observing the donkey.

After a long time, the tiger walked out of the forest and approached the donkey slowly to observe with care. However, the tiger was still a little afraid, and didn't dare to walk too closely.

Suddenly, the donkey raised its head and shouted in a high voice. Scared by the shout, the tiger ran away to a remote place, and didn't dare to come on for a long while.

After a few days, the tiger was already accustomed to the shout of the donkey, and thought there was nothing terrible. So, the tiger moved closer to the donkey, walked around the donkey, but still didn't dare to come at its quarry. Later, the tiger was even closer to the donkey, and collided into the donkey to offend and irritate it on purpose.

Finally, the donkey was annoyed by the tiger, lost its temper, and kicked the tiger with its hoof. This time, the tiger was glad, thinking this guy only had such an ability.

Then, the tiger jumped to pounce the donkey, and bite the donkey's neck. The tiger left with satisfaction after a good meal.

This story comes from *Three Categories of Precepts: A Guizhou Donkey*. The proverb means that a person exhausts its skills, and has no other skills to use.

Repeated Commands

Sun Wu was a renowned militarist in the Spring and Autumn Period (770 BC-476 BC). He Lu, king of the State Wu, convened 180 beauties in his court after hearing Sun Wu was an expert in training the army, and asked Sun Wu to train the beauties.

Sun Wu divided them into two teams, appointed two concubines of He Lu as the captains, and asked each of the beauties to hold a halberd. After the teams stood in place, Sun Wu asked, "Do you know how to turn in different directions?" The women soldiers answer, "Yes, Sir." Then, Sun Wu said again, "To march ahead, you will just look at my breast; to turn left, you will just look at my left hand; to turn right, you will just look at my right hand; and to turn around, you will just look at my back." The women soldiers replied, "Yes, Sir!" Then, Sun Wu ordered the soldiers to fetch the axe (used to kill people in the ancient time), and stressed repeatedly that the military law was merciless, and whoever violated the military law would be severely punished.

Then, Sun Wu beat the drum to issue the command of turning right. However, the women soldiers not only failed to act as ordered, but burst into laughter.

Sun Wu stressed, "If I don't explain the military law clearly, it will be the fault of the general." Then, he explained again what he had told the soldiers in great detail. Then, he beat the drum to issue the command to turn left. The women soldiers still laughed, and treated the command as nothing. Sun Wu said, "It is the fault of the general to explain the rules unclearly. Now that the general has clearly told you what to do, it will be the fault of the captains and soldiers to deny the commands."

So, he ordered other soldiers to push out the two captains and kill them. Seeing Sun Wu would kill his concubines, He Lu hurried to ask Sun Wu to spare them. However, Sun Wu replied, "Now that I am appointed the general, I will no longer accept the command of the king when I fight out." Then, he ordered to kill the two captains, and appointed another two women soldiers in the front of the teams to act as the captains. The women soldiers got so frightened, and knew the military law was not for play. Since then, the women soldiers practiced in earnest turning in different directions, and even such complicated actions as kneeling position and standing up, and didn't dare to play game.

This story comes from *Historical Records: Biography of Sun Tzu and Wu Qi*. Later, people describe Sun Wu's practice of explaining the military law to the women soldiers as "Repeated Commands", which is now used to describe the repeated stress of something to people.

Idiom Stories

Practice Makes Perfect

There was an excellent archer named Chen Yaozi in the Northern Song Dynasty (960-1127).

One day, he practiced archery at home, and hit the target with eight or nine out of ten arrows. The viewers applauded and exclaimed, "Great archery!" Chen Yaozi also felt very pleased. However, an old pitchman selling edible oil nearby just nodded slightly, and didn't think high of Chen's archery.

Chen Yaozi was very unhappy, asking

"Are you also an archer? How do you like my archery?" The pitchman answered candidly, "I don't know archery. You do it ok. However, archery doesn't have any secret. Practice makes perfect." Chen Yaozi became very angry, "What's your skill? How dare you so comment on my archery?"

The old pitchman then took out a copper coin, and covered it on the orifice of a gourd used to contain edibal oil. Then, he fetched a spoon of oil, held the spoon high, and emptied the oil into the guard through the hole in the coin. There was not even a drop of oil beyond the coin hole after the pitchman emptied all the oil. The old man said to Chen Yaozi, "I also have no secret to empty oil, just because I am skillful."

After seeing the pitchman empty oil, Chen Yaozi felt very ashamed. From then on, he never felt complacent again, and practiced the archery with modesty.

This story comes from *Record of Country Life* written by Ouyang Xiu. People have derived the proverb. The proverb means no matter what you do, you will find out many knacks as long as you practice hard and master the rule.

水落石出

Water Falls, Stones Appear

Once upon a time, the housewife of a man was very kind, and always volunteered to help those in need. However, her husband always doubted his wife was doing bad things.

Two brothers, who lost their parents, came to this family from a very remote place. Seeing the brothers were homeless, the wife allowed them to live in the home.

The winter came and cold wind roared. One day, it snowed heavily. On such a cold day, the brothers were so frozen as to tremble because of their rugs. Seeing the poor brothers, the wife showed her pity, and asked them to come into the room to change their clothes so that she would mend the clothes to help them keep warm.

Her husband happened to return home, and saw everything. He couldn't refrain from his doubt, became very unhappy, banged the door and left.

After he returned home, the wife told him, "I just want to help them, but have no other intent. You don't have to doubt this or that. You will eventually understand the truth of the thing, just like stones will naturally appear after water falls."

This story comes from *Ancient Poems: Yange Xing*. The proverb means the stones will naturally show up when water falls down, and compare that the truth of something will emerge when the time comes.

投笔从戎

Renounce the Pay for the Sword

Renounce the Pay
for the Sword

There was a person named Ban Chao in the Eastern Han Dynasty (25-220).

Originally as a scholar, Ban Chao wanted to become a knowledgeable person. Born into a poor family in Xianyang City of Shaanxi Province, he later moved to Luoyang City of Henan Province to make a living.

Having no work to do, Ban Chao went to a government organ and copied instruments to earn some money. He used his salary to feed on himself and his old mother, and thus lived a hard life.

One day, he felt the work of copying instruments was really very boring, and no longer wanted to lead such an average life. He said, "A great man should learn from Fu Jiezi and imitate Zhang Qian, and make the merits in the remote place to win the title of marquis. How can I live such a routine life?"

Throwing away his writing brush, he joined the army. Later, he finally became a general, and was ordered to defend the Western Regions for 31 years, and put down the rebellion launched by Hun nobles a few times, and became a renowned general in the Eastern Han Dynasty.

This story comes from *Later Chronicles of the Han Dynasty: Biography of Ban Chao*. This proverb is later used to describe the fact that scholars give up academic learning to join the army.

完璧归赵

Return the Jade Intact to the State Zhao

Return the Jade Intact to the State Zhao

In the Warring States Period (475 BC-221 BC), King Hui of the State Zhao obtained a rare jade named He's Jade. Hearing the news, the king of the State Qin envied very much, and desired to have it.

Then he had an idea. He thought his state was more powerful than the State Zhao, and then wrote to King Zhao, saying he was willing to exchange He's Jade for 15 towns. In fact, he just wanted to have the treasure through cheating, but didn't really plan to keep his promise.

Though seeing King Qin was playing a trick, King Zhao didn't dare to refuse. They feared that King Qin would attack their country for this excuse. Thus, King Zhao and his ministers were at a loss as to what to do.

Just when King Zhao hesitated, Lin Xiangru, one of his ministers, came to see King Zhao, and said, "Please allow me to take He's Jade to King Qin. If King Qin really gives us 15 towns, I will give him the treasure. Otherwise, I will take the jade back to Your Majesty." King Zhao had to agree.

Lin Xiangru met the King of the Qin State and presented the He's Jade to him. He was so excited to see it that he forgot what he promised.

When seeing King Qin didn't want to keep the promise at all, Lin Xiangru walked to King Qin with calmness, "Your Majesty, this jade has a little flaw. But it is difficult to see it. Please let me show you!"

Believing what Lin Xiangru said, King Qin hurried to return the jade to Lin.

After getting the jade, Lin Xiangru leaned against a column, shouting in a high voice, "I see Your Majesty have no intention to give our king the towns, so I have taken back the jade. If you oblige me, I will knock my head and this jade on the column!"

King Qin got irritated, but feared Lin Xiangru would really break the jade, so said kindly, "We will hold a ceremony in several days to exchange the jade for the towns."

Realizing King Qin was playing a trick again, Lin Xiangru ordered his man to send the jade to the State Zhao in private.

On the day when the ceremony was held, Lin Xiangru said to King Qin calmly, "Your Majesty, I have sent He's Jade back to the State Zhao. If you have the good faith, please first give us the towns, and I will give you He's Jade at once. If you are angry, you may kill me now. However, you still can't have the jade, but all the people will know the State Qin is not believable."

King Qin was so angry as to hit the

ceiling, but had no other choice but allow Lin Xiangru to return home.

This story comes from *Historical Records: Biographies of Lian Po and Lin Xiangru*. Later, people use this proverb to show one manages to return something intact to its owner.

望梅止渴

Quench Thirsty by Longing for Plums

Quench Thirsty by Longing for Plums

Cao Cao was a famous militarist in the Three Kingdoms Period (220-280).

One summer, he led the army for an expedition. At that time, it was very hot, and the sun was shining wildly. The soldiers walked for an entire morning and drank up their water, but there was no water source nearby. The soldiers were tired, thirsty and hot, and almost couldn't march ahead any longer.

Cao Cao ordered the solders to look for water everywhere, but failed. Having no other choice, Cao Cao asked soldiers to dig a well. The soldiers dug a very deep well but no water was found. The soldiers lay on the ground, and didn't want to walk any more. Cao Cao was very anxious — if the army stayed in this place, the soldiers would run up their vitality, and could die here because of thirsty. He must think of an idea to make the soldiers move on!

An idea suddenly came to him. He climbed to a high place, looked around, and shouted to the soldiers, "Water! Water!"

Hearing the shout of their general, the soldiers, who were suffering thirst bitterly, immediately stood up from the ground. Cao Cao said, "Just now, I had a look at this place. I went this way before. There is a plum forest just on the other side of the hill. The plums are big and sweet, and we can enjoy the plums as many as we can. Then, will we still be thirsty?"

Hearing his remarks, the soldiers refreshed themselves, and slavered when

Idiom Stories

thinking of the acidic plums. They didn't feel as bad as before. Cao Cao then made use of this opportunity to lead his army to march ahead, and finally reached the destination.

In fact, there was no plum forest at all, and it was just a small trick played by Cao Cao.

This story comes from *Essays and Criticism*. Later, this proverb is used to describe that when a wish can't com true, somebody will have to console himself with daydreaming.

Lament Before the Vast Sea

He Bo was the Yellow River God in the fairy tale. One autumn, a very heavy rain came, and all the small rivers were full of water, which flowed into the Yellow River from all directions.

The Yellow River became much broader all of a sudden, and flowed eastwards with surging waves. Seeing such vast and surging water, He Bo felt very proud, and thought all the grand things in the world belonged to him.

He Bo traveled eastwards with

excitement with the river water, until he reached the East China Sea.

Looking at the vast sea, He Bo saw surging waves and the sea was too enormous to see the border. Compared to the rivers on the land, the sea was much, much larger. At this time, He Bo realized his littleness in face of the vast sea. Looking around and looking at the sky, he sighed, and said to the god of the sea, "I am just the person who thinks himself wise because of the limited view. I heard some rumors before, saying the knowledge of Confucius was still limited, though he was very witted; and Bo Yi was still not very generous, though he gave up his territory. I didn't believe these remarks in the past, but today I believe them when I see the sea. Those remarks are not false. I had never been to the sea before, and had no idea the sea was so extensive. Instead, I thought I myself was the most splendid. My knowledge was really limited!"

This story comes from *Chuang Tze: Autumn River*. Originally, this proverb meant a person broadened his vision in face of great things, and felt his littleness, and now is used to describe the insufficient strength needed to do something.

胸有成竹

Have a Finished Bamboo in the Mind

Idiom Stories

159

Have a Finished Bamboo in the Mind

Wen Tong, a famous artist in the Northern Song Dynasty (960-1127), was particularly expert at drawing bamboos. The bamboos he drew were vivid, and just resembled the bamboos that grow on the ground.

Wen Tong had spent much work on drawing bamboos. To portrait bamboos vividly, Wen Tong planted a bamboo forest in front of his window, but he was not anxious to draw them. As long as he had time, he would observe various shapes of the bamboos before the window. He observed what small bamboos were like and large bamboos were like; and what they were like in wind or rain.

After the long-term observation, Wen Tong developed a complete understanding of the characteristics of bamboos. He knew how the bamboos would move in wind, and how bamboo leaves shook in rain. All in all, he mastered every tiny change and feature of those bamboos from A to Z.

Only until now, he picked up the painting brush to draw vivid bamboos without stop.

This is because he had an insight into various shapes of bamboos, and knew what the bamboos were like and the properties of this plant. So, his friend praised him, "When Wen Tong draws bamboos, he has the finished bamboos in his mind. The bamboos he draws are very vivid." "Have a finished bamboo in the mind" means he had developed the perfect image of the bamboos before he drew them.

This story comes from *A Collection of Chicken Ribs*. The proverb originally meant that an intact image of the bamboos was already built in the mind, and later is used to describe a person who has devised a mature plan before doing something or much confidence in himself or others.

A Whole Heart

There was a person named Yi Qiu, who played the game of I-go best in his country, in the Spring and Autumn Period (770 BC-476 BC).

Two persons learned the game from Yi Qiu. One was very attentive, caught every word his teacher told him, and spent all of his energy on learning the game. Another person thought the game of I-go was not very difficult to learn, and so he was not very serious, though he also followed Yi Qiu for the skill. When holding chessmen in his hand, he was thinking about the birds flying in the sky and how to shoot them down.

Though they learned from the same teacher, the second person was never the match for the first person. Is this because of his intelligence?

Certainly not. Playing the game of I-go was just a small skill, but one couldn't become an expert in the skill if he failed to focus any of his energy on learning. The person was diverted from his learning, so he certainly lost to another person.

This proverb comes from *Mencius: Gaozi Part One*, and means a whole heart and concentration of energies.